P9-DHB-043

A Week in Aya's World:

THE IVORY COAST

CROWELL-COLLIER PRESS
Collier-Macmillan Limited, London

A Week in Aya's World: THE IVORY COAST

Photographs and text by Marc and Evelyne Bernheim

 Library of Congress Catalog Card Number: 70–75391 • The Macmillan Company • Collier-Macmillan Canada Ltd., Toronto, Ontario • Printed in the United States of America • First Printing

Photographs from Rapho Guillumette Pictures

Monday morning Aya is up at 6. Aya lives in the Ivory Coast, in a big city called Abidjan. She lives with her parents, four brothers, and an older sister. Her favorite is Baby Mo. She washes him in a basin. He loves the cool water trickling down his back.

Aya's skirt is all wet. She has to change her dress. "Hurry Aya! Come and get your hair done before school." Mother twists and turns Aya's hair into six little braids.

School is near Aya's house.
The girls wear special dresses
in class. Today Teacher wants
Aya to start the reading exercises.
All children of the Ivory
Coast learn French in school.

After school, Aya helps Mother
prepare the meal. At home
Aya often wears a long African
gown. She pounds the yams
in a wood mortar, while
Mother cooks the fish in hot
"pili-pili" sauce. They are eaten
together and called "foufou."

All that pounding in a long
gown has made Aya very hot.
She puts on her playdress
and calls her brothers and
sister. "Foufou is ready!"

After the meal Father helps Aya with her homework. He wants every one of his children to get good grades.

"Have you forgotten?" Mother calls. "We are all having our picture taken." Mother pulls a clean dress out of Aya's closet. This is just a little suitcase. Though Aya has only four dresses, she loves to change them all the time.

612

Father has put on
his great robe for the
family portrait. Now
everyone is waiting
for Little Mo to stop
giggling.

Tuesday morning Aya is very noisy in class. "Silence!" shouts Teacher.

To punish her, Teacher sends Aya to the blackboard. She must write out "I promise to be good," twenty times in her neatest handwriting.

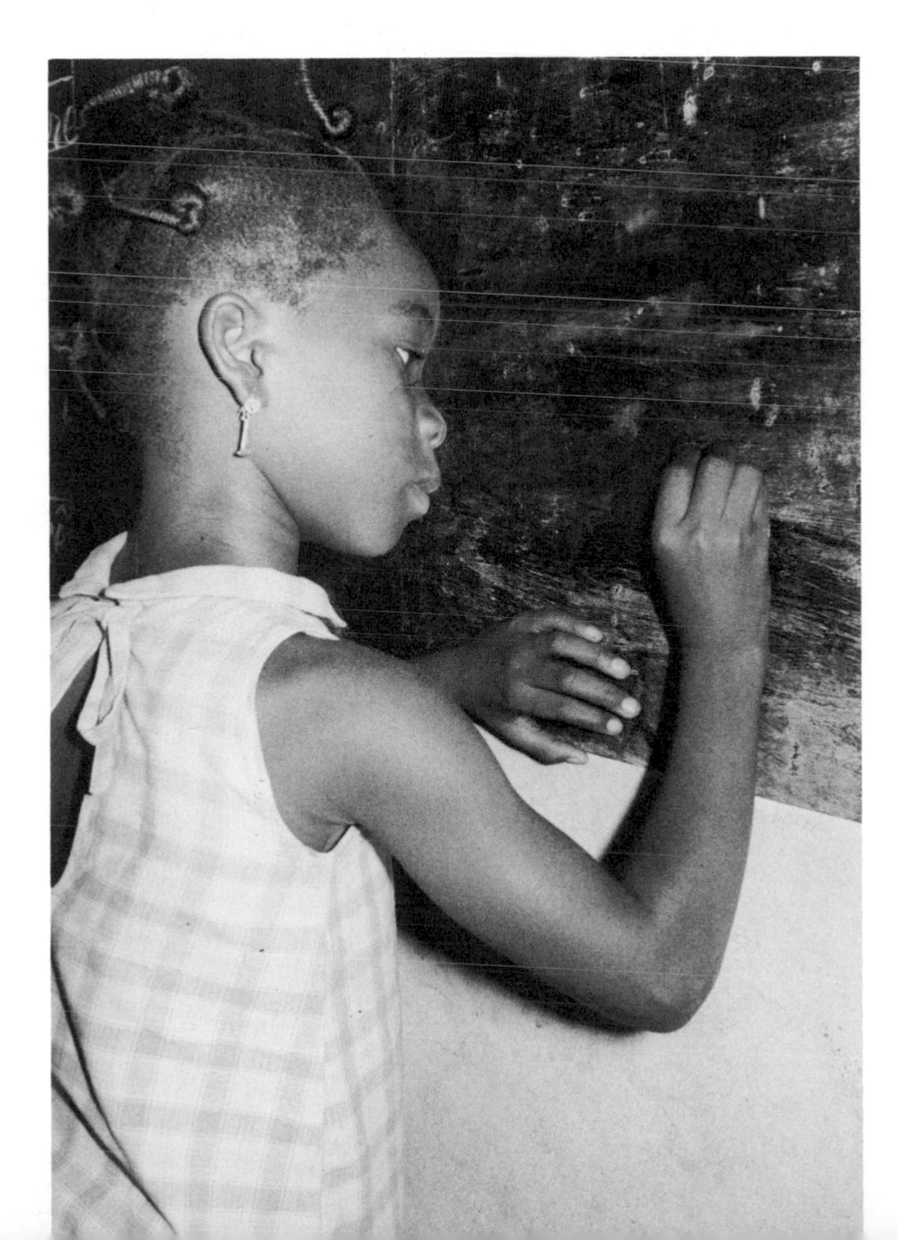

At noon she leaves school with all the first-graders for lunch at home and a little nap.

Aya has told only her brother Tiro about what happened in school. Everyone rests under the pepper tree, but Aya feels sad because she was scolded.

In the afternoon Aya goes back to school early to finish up her task before Teacher returns. Her work looks so neat on the blackboard. Teacher is very pleased.

No more school work for today! The class goes out to play Blindman's Buff.

After school Aya goes with her mother to the big yard near home to pound bananas for supper.

On Wednesday school is out early. Aya and Tiro can help Mother with the shopping. At the big outdoor market there is always something new to learn and see.

Marketing is fun, but it is time to go home.

After lunch Aya grabs her best friend. "Let's go, Api!"

Together with her other friends, Gaby and Caroline, they play riddles, and "Ata-plata-pla," ring-round-the-rosy, with all the children.

Later in the day she plays
"mpe-mpe," hop-and-skip.

Then she sets up her little market stand
and sells powdered milk to friends.
It is a penny for a spoonful.

Tonight it is too hot to sit indoors.
Aya brings out a blackboard and
teaches Little Cesar how to read,
just as she learned in school.

On Thursday school is always closed.
Aya and her friends buy charcoal
for their mothers' cooking fires.

Tiro has no school either. Off they go to see Father. He has promised to take them to the harbor where he works to see all the big ships.

Father counts the bags of cocoa beans before they are loaded on ships sailing to America. In America the beans will be made into chocolate. Aya knows that cocoa beans grow on trees in her country's forests, but she has never tasted chocolate.

In the afternoon Aya goes to the Museum with Tiro and her friends. They all take turns at playing musical notes on the "balafon."

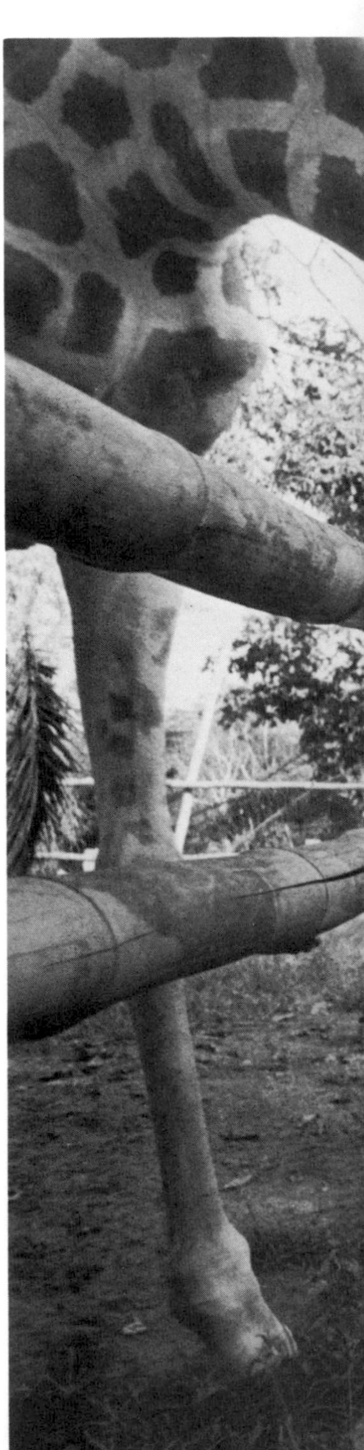

Then Aya makes a special trip to the zoo to visit her friend the giraffe. He likes to scoop up sugar cubes from her hand.

Friday morning Aya is doing her arithmetic. Suddenly the principal walks in to look at everyone's copybook. He asks Aya to come to his office after class. Aya is a little scared. She has never been to the principal's office.

"Come in Aya! Don't be afraid! I have decided to give you a new copybook because you have the best handwriting in the class."

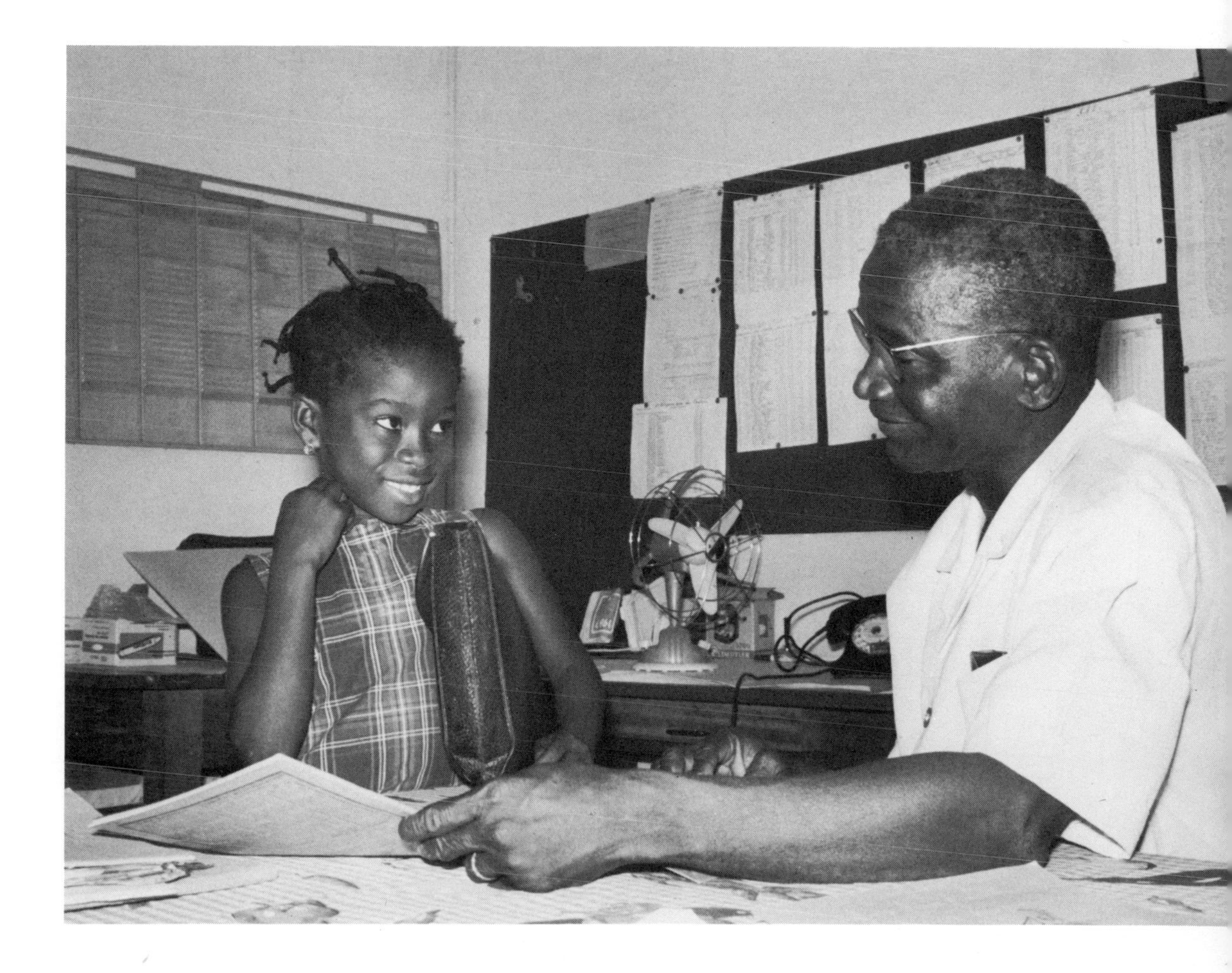

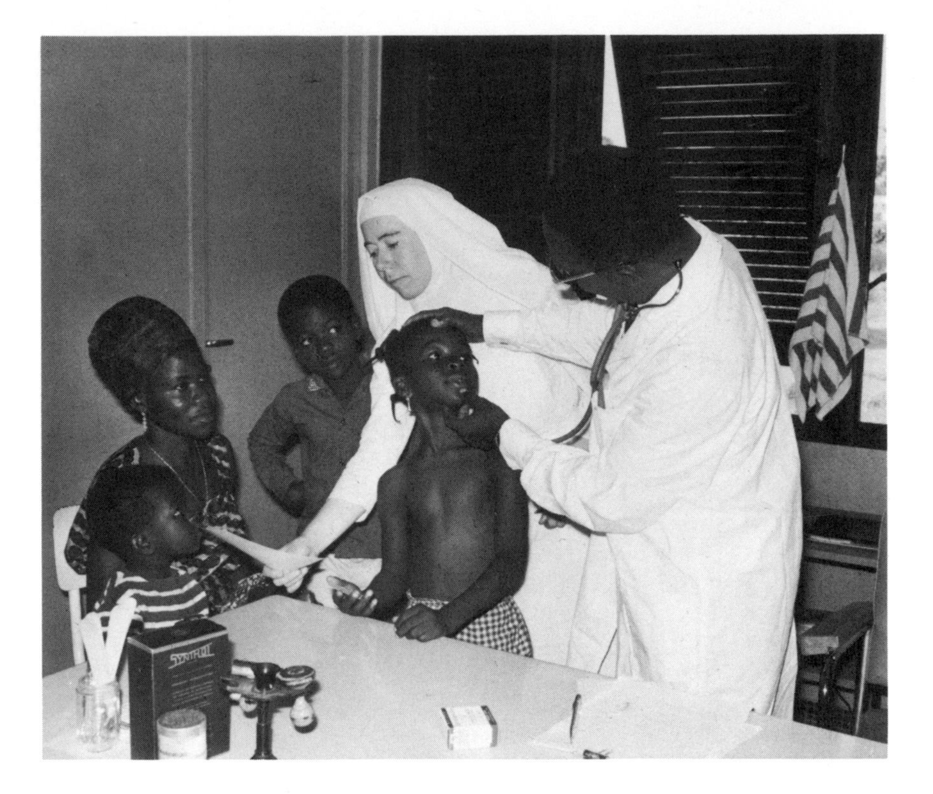

After school Mother takes her
family to the doctor for a
checkup.

Aya returns home and finds
Little Mo crying. She takes him
on her back and wraps
him tightly in a cloth to walk
him around the block.

Later Cousin Koko
comes over to
Aya's house.
Together they
cook supper,

and play African checkers in front of the house.

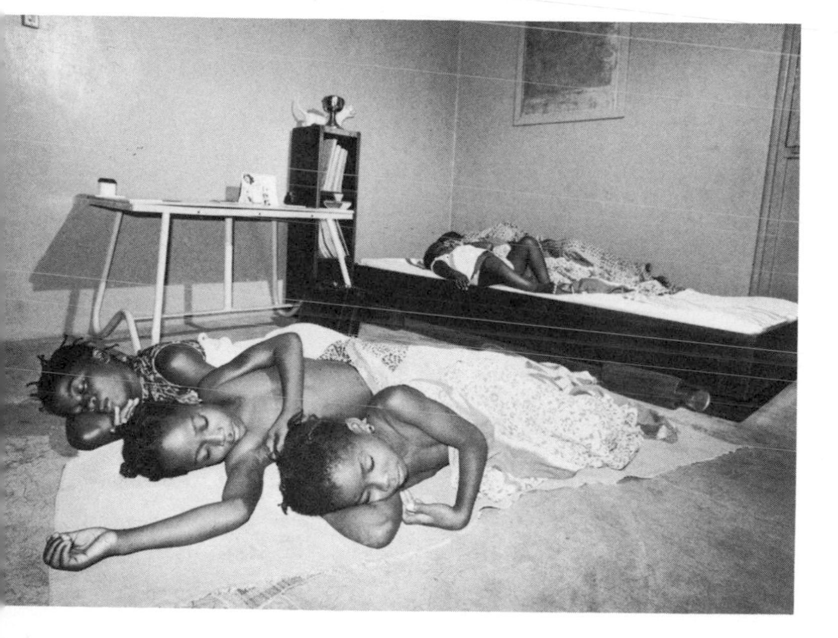

Koko stays overnight. All the girls sleep on the floor. The boys sleep on the bed. Goodnight Aya! Sleep well Koko!

Tonight Aya has a dream: she is racing with Tiro on the beach. . . . When will Father take them to the sea again?

Saturday is the day for settling all the week's quarrels. So Aya fights with her friend Caroline.

But then, it's so nice to make up!

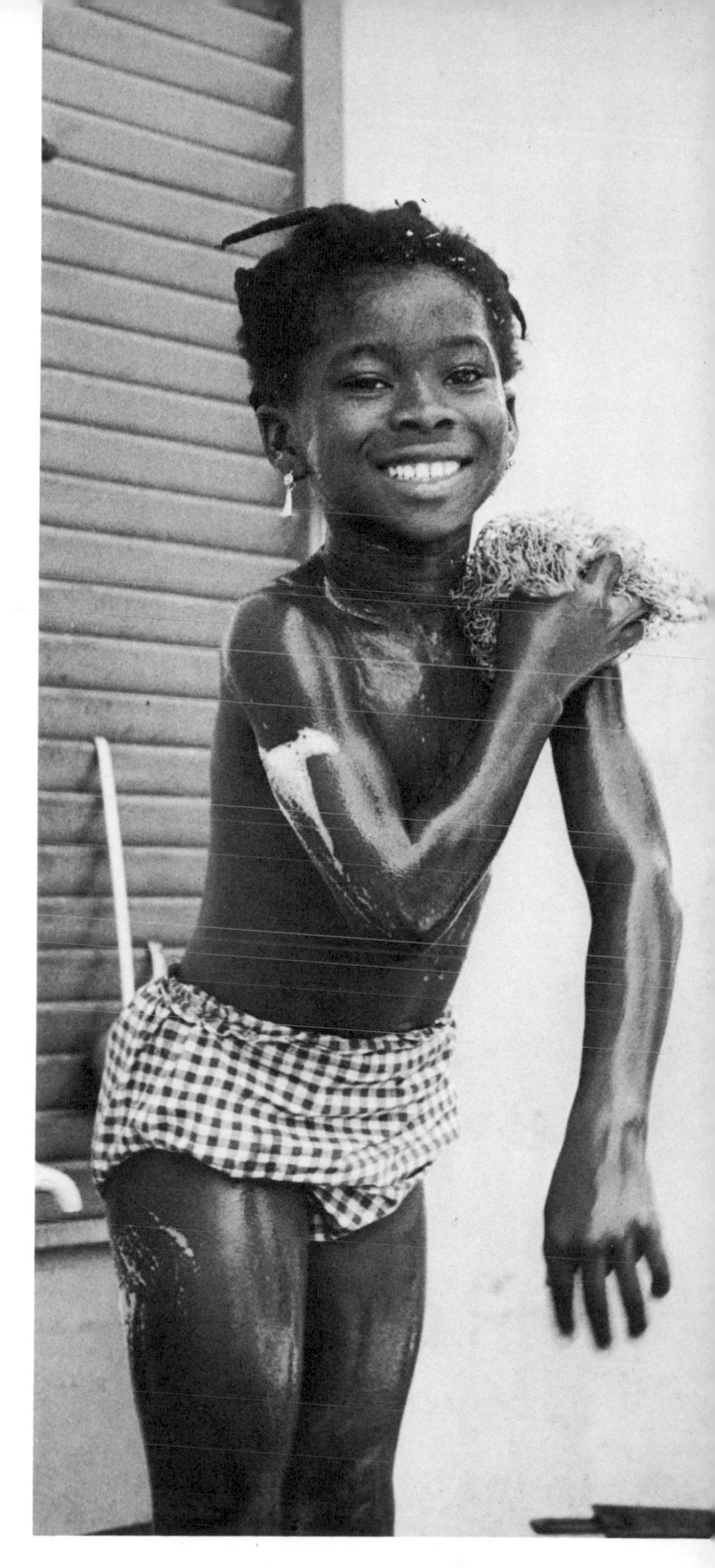

There is just time to wash
up for the dance at
Uncle Fanta's house.

At her uncle's the men play on different drums, big and small. Uncle Fanta dances with Aya.

This drum is called a "tam-tam." It is taller than Aya. Father tilts the drum so she can play it.

Back home the family gathers in the living room before going to bed. Father tells Aya there will be a surprise tomorrow.

Sunday morning, as they leave church,
Father tells Aya and Tiro about his surprise.

This is it: a boat ride to visit cousin Lucy in her village! Aya can hardly wait. She has never left the city. She has never been to a village. She does not even know Cousin Lucy!

Lucy is waiting for them by the shore. She shows Aya her village, and takes her to meet Grandmother who is very, very old,

while Tiro joins Lucy's brothers in a game of tug of war.

Then Lucy takes Aya to the forest. Together they get fresh water from the brook and carry it back in buckets to the house.

All this is new to Aya. In the city, she just opens a faucet and out flows the water!

It's time to go home. Cousin Lucy walks Aya back to the shore. "Lucy, will you come to visit me in the city?" Aya asks.

On the long ride back across the lagoon,
Aya wonders what the next week
will bring. She jumps out of the boat.

Aya is so happy. She can hardly wait to tell Mother, and Teacher, and all her friends about this wonderful day.